FAUST

Opera in Four Acts

Music by
Charles-François Gounod

Libretto by
MICHEL CARRE
and
JULES BARBIER
After the poem by Goethe

English Version by
RUTH and THOMAS MARTIN

ED. 2679

G. SCHIRMER, INC.
New York

Note

G. SCHIRMER, INC.

609 Fifth Avenue
New York 17, N. Y.

FAUST

Breathe the name of Faust and Devil-smoke may curl from a neighbor's ear, so universal has become the legend of the man who sold his spirit to the powers of evil. Yet Faust is a modern addition to the age-old story of black magic, to the tale immemorial of the outcast who has gone at witching hour to a crossroads and there, standing within a burning circle traced by his own staff, called Satan to his aid. Across the centuries, Mediterranean lands and their races have been less responsive to this type of magic than the gloomier tribes to the North. Italy has produced no famous wizards; practitioners of magic in Spain were gypsies, rather than natives; and even Gothic France felt no vogue for the supernatural. The adepts at black magic flourished in Germany, the British Isles, Scandinavia, the Slavic countries, and that seventeenth-century haven for witches, Massachusetts.

Into this caldron of the ages stepped Faust — a man who actually lived in Germany between 1480 and 1540. Some confusion exists about his Christian name, recorded variously as Georg and Johann,[1] impelling historians not long ago to the belief that two Hell-bent individuals, bearing the identical surname, must have flourished at the same time. Modern research has reduced them to one, the name varying with the places visited.

One thing is certain: despite all possible ambiguities, Faust made a definite impact on the people of his time. An unscrupulous and thoroughly immoral fortune-teller, teacher and wizard, he attended the University of Heidelberg (B.A., 1509) and studied divinity at Wittenberg. "But," as an old English account put it, soon after his demise, "Faustus being of a naughty minde and otherwise addicted, applied not his studies, but took himself to other exercises". Charged with gross misconduct while teaching in a boys' school at Kreuznach (a document of the time refers to him as "the great necromancer and sodomite"), he beat a retreat in order to escape the law, refused a safe conduct to Nuremberg in 1532, and boasted continually of his prowess in the magic arts, referring to the Devil as his brother-in-law, and offering — for a sum — to reveal the future. At one point, he predicted that a colonial expedition bound for Venezuela in 1540 would meet with failure, and he was proved to be right. Ultimately, the man is said to have met a frightful death.

For the most part, Faust was a notorious character whose suspected links to Satan overshadowed any real attainments in his lifetime. Stories about his sins proliferated. He was alleged, for example, to have raised the ghost of Helen of Troy and cohabited with her. This feat, combined with other tales of the supernatural, inflamed the German public and gave quick rise to Faust's universal association with the damned. Almost immediately after his death, he became the hero of a literary tract — the *Faustbuch* — by Johann Spies (the book was published at Frankfurt-am-Main in 1587), describing his pact with the Devil. There followed a second *Faustbuch*, this one by Georg Rudolf Widmann; and confusion was heightened for a time through the popular association of Johann Fust, co-inventor of printing, with the infernal Johann Faust.

The *Faust* cult soon spread to England. Spies' book was translated almost at once by a British scholar with the cryptic pen-name of "P. F., Gent."; and shortly

---

[1] Goethe, in the epic play which took this man's pact with the Devil as its point of departure, changed his name to Heinrich.

thereafter, inspired by this translation, appeared the celebrated play of Christopher Marlowe: *The Tragicall History of Dr. Faustus*. Back went the expanded subject to Germany, transformed — through the genius of Marlowe — into an evolving part of the Teutonic *Faust* tradition. Supposedly, the play was given in Frankfurt during the 1590's. Historic performance dates exist at Graz in 1608 and Dresden, 1626.

Marlowe, in this magnificent fresco of a play (modern scholars are not agreed as to the reconstruction of all its details), incorporated the raising of Helen of Troy — "Was this the face that launch'd a thousand ships?" — invested Mephistopheles with a certain impish humor (notably in the Roman episode when Faust and the Devil, disguised as cardinals, give the Pope a hard time); but most importantly, from the standpoint of this tale's evolution into the great morality play by Goethe, Faust is pictured as one who — through virtue and knowledge — at one time helped whole cities escape the plague.[2] Ennui, restlessness of soul have led him into sin.

Basic, in the development of this tale, is Faust's preoccupation with a Classical past. Strong hints of Grecian learnings (so prominent in the second part of Goethe's play) are already marked in the tragedy by Marlowe. Not only does the magician, aided by Mephistopheles, raise the ghost of Helen. He also brings to earth — though fleetingly — the spirits of Alexander the Great and the hero's paramour.

In the Marlowe play, as in all older versions of the legend, Faust is irrevocably damned. Though repentant at the end and praying to the Lord, he is snatched away by the Devil. The Satanic high command appears divided: Lucifer appearing briefly, is the top-level fiend; Beelzebub, his chief lieutenant; and Mephistopheles, a trusted subordinate. By the time this story reached the Romantic era, Mephistopheles alone would hold sway.

The *Faust* tale, enormously popular in the German theater of the 1600's, fell subject to many different treatments, some of them crossed with the comic traditions of Harlequin. All sorts of variations on the original theme took over. It was not, however, until the end of the eighteenth century that the crowning idea of Faust's redemption was advanced. The philosopher-playwright, Gotthold Lessing, is credited as having been the first great name associated with the salvation of Faust. He left, as part of an uncompleted manuscript, a scheme pointing toward the magician's reconciliation with God — a project developed to the fullest by Johann Wolfgang von Goethe (1749-1832).

Goethe's *Faust* is more a weighing of life itself than a theatrical absolute. In Part I of the drama — published in 1808 — the German master lay stress on the emotional element in his hero's career, embodied by the maiden Margarethe (Gretchen): sinned against, corrupted, and yet redeemed. Then in Part II, written years later and completed shortly before Goethe's death, he shifted emphasis to Faust's relations with the world, his attempt to fit into the scheme of universal being, and his final escape from evil through dedication to the welfare of his fellow humans.[3] . . . As in the play by Marlowe, Helen of Troy appears . . . but here the mating of Faust and Helen takes on the symbolic quality of a union between the Europe of a later day and the golden clarity of ancient Greece. Their child Euphorion, like Icarus before him, tries to rise above the earth and, flying too high, perishes.

[2] In the play by Goethe (Part I), mention is made by grateful townspeople of the part played by Faust's father in a similar emergency.

[3] In the memorable epilogue to Part II, one of the monuments of world drama, Margarethe is seen as a Penitent, interceding for Faust at the gates of Heaven.

It has been said that Goethe, in the character of this youth born through the mating of different eras and doomed to an early end, meant to personify the poet Byron.

Although since the time of Goethe the *Faust* legend has moved chiefly in the musical arena, it has also been continued in literature by Adelbert von Chamisso, Christian Grabbe, Nikolaus Lenau (these latter two combining the old story with that of another arch-delinquent, Don Juan), Heinrich Heine . . . and, more recently, Paul Valéry and Thomas·Mann. A tale of which the essence is Man and the Devil should be able to keep indefinitely gathering new shapes, forms and variations in every corner of narrative art.

The first of many operas on the *Faust* story — by Ludwig Spohr, produced in 1818 — drew not upon the Goethe play but on sixteenth-century sources. A success in its time, the work has long since disappeared, yielding ground to more vital treatments of the legend. Two other famous operas of the period, though not handling the *Faust* subject, made strong use of an associated theme. Karl Maria von Weber's *Der Freischütz* (1820), a fascinating piece of theater magic concerned with forests, the hunt, and sorcery, centered its plot about an infernal wraith named Samiel, in reality the Archfiend; and Giacomo Meyerbeer's *Robert le Diable* (1831) forged for the first time the now traditional bond between bassos and diabolical rôles (the leading tenor in this opera, Robert, ranks only as a half-devil . . . whereas his basso father, Bertram, is the genuine article). But the source for modern satanic repertoire in general and of the *Faust* story in particular remains the play by Goethe.

The master himself loved music; and in tribute to Mozart, whose works he adored, he contrived a sequel to *The Magic Flute*. As for an opera on *Faust*, Goethe declared that only the great Wolfgang Amadeus might have come close to an ideal setting of the play. Composers of the nineteenth century did not much interest him — strangely, for a man whose most celebrated drama transcended in concept all limitations of time and place. . . . And yet distinguished musicians of the age were linked to the play, even if not by Goethe. Beethoven is said to have been approached by the publishers, Breitkopf and Härtel, with a commission for incidental music in the manner of his score for *Egmont*, but nothing came of the project. When it was suggested to Meyerbeer that he turn his hand to setting Part I of the drama, the noted composer replied: "*Faust* is the Ark of the Convenant, a sanctuary not to be approached with profane music". Among the more exotic might-have-beens was a plan, which came to naught, for an operatic *Faust* with libretto by Alexandre Dumas and music by Rossini. A wilder mating of talents would be hard to imagine.

As the age of program music developed in the concert hall, so did the idea of *Faust* grow in appeal to symphonically-minded composers. By now Goethe's Gretchen had become an inseparable part of the tale, and she was to prevail in two of the more famous orchestral treatments. Thus Richard Wagner, as one of his earliest — and finest — works devised *A Faust Overture*, in essence a symphonic poem, alternating and contrasting two principal themes: the turbulent Faust and the idealized Gretchen. Franz Liszt was later to build an entire symphony on this subject, with a unique three-movement construction: the opening Allegro — tense, somber and troubled — evoking a portrait of Faust; the Andante, a lovely, introspective sketch of Margarethe; and the finale, a satanic parody by Mephistopheles on both preceding movements — since the Devil, "the Spirit who denies", can have no positive identity of his own. At its climax, the symphony passes to a tender reprise of the Gretchen motive as solo tenor and male chorus sing the closing words of *Faust*, Part II:

"The eternal feminine leads us on". . . . Two enormous canvases for chorus and orchestra, also based on the Goethe play, were provided by Robert Schumann in his *Scenes from Faust,* and Gustav Mahler in the second portion of his Symphony No. 8 ("Symphony of a Thousand"). Both Schumann and Mahler have set the mystical epilogue to music with strikingly different but innately moving results.

In the borderland between opera and concert lies the famous cantata by Berlioz, *The Damnation of Faust.* Although following in most respects Part I of Goethe's play, it casts aside one deep-seated concept of the drama: the hero is not saved, but damned. Aside from this notable departure (for which Berlioz pleads a reversion to Marlowe), *The Damnation* offers perhaps the most consistent synthesis in music of Goethe's masterpiece. It is definitely *not* an opera, even though brought on stage many years after Berlioz's death by a well-meaning but misguided adapter (Raoul Gunsbourg — Monte Carlo, 1893). The work — a concert piece — remains episodic, subjective, "interior" in every respect, with the visual elements best left, as the composer intended, to the imagination of the listener.

Opera itself has brought us (skipping a dozen or more forgotten works on this subject) the highly successful *Faust* (1859) of Gounod; Boito's *Mefistofele* (1868, revised 1875), including scenes from both parts of the vast drama by Goethe, with Gretchen (here named Margherita) and Helen of Troy as the dual heroines; and Busoni's *Doktor Faust* (posthumous, 1925), a strongly individual approach to the legend, which has been gathering fame in the past few years. As a bit of interesting by-play, the characters of Faust and Mephistopheles appear in Prokofieff's opera *The Flaming Angel* (1919), set in Germany at the time of the original legend. Although the pair comes into sight only briefly, it is clear — by the end of the work — that Mephistopheles has motivated the whole gruesome cycle of events. For modern tastes, Boito and Busoni may evoke a more exciting and sulphurous quality than the kindly Gounod; but as a favorite with audiences, an indestructible commodity, *Faust* continues to hold the palm.

It is quite unlikely that among the host of composers, both operatic and symphonic, drawn to the Faust legend any could have been less inclined by nature toward the diabolical than Charles-François Gounod (1818-1893). He was an amiable, placid person, of a family devoted to the arts. Gounod's father, a painter, had placed second in the Grand Prix de Rome during his youth and later in life was entrusted with restoring certain of the canvases in the Louvre. The mother was musical. In addition to the artistic flair absorbed from both his parents, Gounod also carried within him a strong religious bent which, after his student days in Paris and a time in Rome as winner of the Grand Prix, led in the direction of church music. On returning to France from his Roman studies, he became organist and choirmaster at the Missions Étrangères, also pursuing a course in theology. The span of 1845-'50 has been described as his years of silence, so immersed did he become in matters of religion.

It took the great Pauline Viardot-García, one of the leading singers of Europe, to bring him out of his shell. This extraordinary artist who had created the part of Fidès in Meyerbeer's *Le Prophète,* held the friendship of Berlioz and many other eminent composers, was the confidante of top figures in the literary world, and commanded enormous respect at the Paris Opéra, reacted with interest when the young Gounod was brought to play his music for her. In 1851 it was she who appeared in his first stage work, *Sapho,* launched in grandeur at the big opera house. From then on, Gounod's career in the theater — though not an overnight success — was assured.

In the following year this composer, responding to his great love for sacred music, became conductor of the Orphéon choral society in Paris, a post which he held for eight years. Yet the pursuit of conducting did not stay his hand at composition. In 1854 he brought off *La Nonne Sanglante*, an unsuccessful work, at the Paris Opéra. Four years later he was engaged by the Théâtre-Lyrique — a forward-looking junior opera house — to compose music for *Faust*, with text by Jules Barbier and Michel Carré.

This was an assignment of which Gounod long had dreamed. His proposed idea on the subject had previously been turned down by Alphonse Royer, director of the Imperial Academy of Music, because: "Cela manquait de pompe".[4] And so he fell in eagerly with the venture planned for the Théâtre-Lyrique. While Gounod was at work on the score of *Faust*, word came suddenly via the Paris theatrical grapevine that a new dramatic version of the tale by a playwright named d'Ennery was to be mounted at the Théâtre de la Porte Saint Martin. Fearing an unnecessary and perhaps ruinous competition, Léon Carvalho, director of the Théâtre-Lyrique, persuaded Gounod and his collaborators to suspend work on *Faust* and turn their attention, for the moment, to another project. After a week, according to his Memoirs, of agitation and soul-searching, the composer agreed and started work on a musical adaptation of Molière's comedy, *Le Médècin Malgré Lui*, successfully produced that same year.

The new play by d'Ennery at Porte Saint Martin met with less acclaim than had been expected. At last it folded its tents, and the Théâtre-Lyrique was ready to proceed with *Faust*. When the score had moved to completion, rehearsals went all ways but smoothly. Whole scenes were suppressed, on demand of the management. The usually amiable Gounod was up in arms about cuts . . . but they were made.

A thoroughly distinguished audience was on hand for the opera's opening night, March 19, 1859. Auber, Berlioz, Delacroix, Pasdeloup, Heugel were among the many leaders of the arts in attendance. Reaction in general proved good but not ecstatic. Berlioz, in his capacity as music critic, wrote in the *Journal des Débats* of "the great and legitimate success obtained by Gounod". He liked especially the simplicity of Marguerite's entrance in the Kermesse; the lovely line of Faust's aria, "Salut, demeure"; and, above all, the poetic ending of the garden scene, with Marguerite's rapturous "Il m'aime!" The performance itself varied in quality. Marie Miolan-Carvalho, wife of the theater's director, sang Marguerite and pleased the public greatly. Until that evening she had been heard only in comic opera, and three years before the première of *Faust* had drawn this unflattering review: "A thin, shrill soprano, as slender as her person, cut in two by three or four pasty notes, a regular bird-pipe". Mme. Carvalho evidently made progress, in the face of this notice, to the point where she was equipped to fill a demanding rôle, for her Marguerite was distinctly a success. As for the tenor, Gounod had set his heart on the engagement of a personable lyric artist named Guardi, who developed vocal troubles in rehearsal, had to withdraw, and left the management looking for another tenor who might quickly learn the part. For a time Gounod himself, possessor of a small but serviceable voice, considered taking over the rôle; but at last Joseph Barbot, a tenor of middle years, teaching at the Conservatoire, stepped in and filled the gap.

---

[4] "That's not showy enough."

The other principals in this performance were on the adequate rather than brilliant side.

Despite such inequalities of fortune, *Faust* began to build a public. In its early days at the Théâtre-Lyrique, pages of spoken dialogue linked the musical numbers; but for a production of 1860 in Strasbourg, Gounod turned the work into a formal grand opera by replacing all dialogue with sung recitatives. The French musicologist, Paul Landormy, speculates that the so-called "new" version of Strasbourg might indeed have followed Gounod's original plan, since long before Carvalho's invitation to the Théâtre-Lyrique, the composer had dreamed of placing his score at the Opéra, where absence of spoken dialogue was *de rigueur*.

A strange history follows. Owing to theatrical intrigues of various sorts, *Faust* was not performed in Paris from 1859 to 1862. The Théâtre-Lyrique had failed, its doors were closed. Both the new score and its well known Marguerite, Mme. Carvalho, were barred from the stage of the rival Opéra-Comique. An unexpected stroke of good luck, however, retrieved Gounod's fortunes. During the opera's first year, its authors had gone looking for a publisher. It was not easy to find one until Antoine de Choudens, then a beginner in the business, offered his entire capital of 10,000 francs for the rights. In addition, he arranged for performances of *Faust* throughout Germany, where it had a marked success. Returning to Paris, the work proceeded in triumph to a Théâtre-Lyrique newly reorganized by Carvalho. Choudens, in full justice, was to reap a fortune.

At last, in 1869, came the call for which Gounod had waited. Foreign acclaim had touched his opera not only in Germany, where Munich and Stuttgart received it with acclaim, but in Belgium, England,[5] Italy and America.[6] Now a famous international property, its presence was requested on the stage of the Paris Opéra. Through the previous addition of recitatives for the Strasbourg production of 1860, all was formally in order for its presentation in the big house. Only one item was lacking: a full-scale ballet, of which Paris Opéra audiences were traditionally fond. And so a dance episode was added (Act IV, Scenes 1-3), dipping ambivalently into both the Walpurgisnacht of the original play's Part I, with its witchlike fury, and the shining Classical Sabbath of Part II. To offset Faust's distress at dour medieval demons, Mephistopheles causes the famous courtesans of history (including Cleopatra) to appear before him; and here, as a prima ballerina, materializes Helen of Troy: agile, glittering and silent in her white *tutu*.

The remodeled *Faust* traveled first to the old opera house on Rue Pelletier, in use during the Second Empire; and then, with the opening in the early 1870's of the lavish new theater built by Garnier, it became a fixture of the Parisian musical stage, a synonym for all that was melodious and dazzling in lyric drama. Full of recognizable tunes from one end to the other, devilish in its plot without requiring any sense of audience identification, turned out with a fine sense of vocal effectiveness (great singers of the time loved it), and above all never taxing the esthetic responses of a public that wanted to be entertained, *Faust* soon bestrode the Western World. It is said that Queen Victoria adored the work, and one can understand why. On the opening night of New York's Metropolitan Opera House

[5] During this opera's second season in the British capital, Gounod introduced a new aria for baritone, "Avant de quitter ces lieux", in tribute to the singing of Sir Charles Santley, who had created the rôle of Valentin in London one year previously.

[6] Launched on a multilingual toboggan, *Faust* had been introduced to New York (November, 1863) in Italian and, later that same month, to Philadelphia in German.

— October 22, 1883 — *Faust* was chosen as the inaugural score. Christine Nilsson, who had created Marguerite in the Paris Opéra version, was on hand to bring authenticity (although the work was sung, on this occasion, in Italian). Restored, with the passing of years, to its original French, *Faust* became a vehicle for the greatest of Metropolitan singers: Emma Eames, Nellie Melba, Lillian Nordica, Geraldine Farrar, Elisabeth Rethberg prominent among the Marguerites; Jean de Reszke and Enrico Caruso as historic Fausts; Lawrence Tibbett and John Charles Thomas as Valentin; Édouard de Reszke, Pol Plançon, and Feodor Chaliapin as notable interpreters of Mephistopheles. Over a span of forty years — dating from that gala first night until the decade after World War I — no opera may be said to have enjoyed more solid audience popularity. Then the falling away began. The melodies so full of charm impressed a younger generation as cloying. Gounod's sense of the dramatic — especially in the diabolical sequences — was found to lack bite. Perhaps at the root of it all lay the disappearance of the supple, aristocratic vocal style asociated with earlier New York performances. In any event, *Faust* — though still on the list of favorite operas — lost ground in audience affection. During the last season in the old house (1965-'66), the Metropolitan revived the score as a sentimental gesture, with a backward look to the opening night of 1883. Public response was loyal but not overwhelming.

In Germany and Austria, where the work still attracts, it is billed invariably as *Margarethe,* as if to imply that this imported opera must not be confused with a national treasure: the Goethe spoken play. For the guardians of the Ark, Gounod's approach is lopsided. In dwelling on romantic aspects, he has stripped the drama of its philosophic point. But for judges less harsh, the Gretchen element, set to music with so much sensitivity, provides survival power. Long after Mephistopheles has strutted his final exit and Faust carolled his attractive tunes, it is the deeply felt, movingly sympathetic treatment of the heroine that comes through in a great performance. The ending of the garden episode, so justly hailed by Berlioz; the Church Scene in which Marguerite, tormented by the Devil, intones a prayer that soars above orchestra, chorus and organ; and the girl's madness that precedes the closing trio . . . all these, with the presence of a first-class Marguerite, can evoke for us some of the fervor that must have been experienced by audiences of a former day.

That Gounod was definitely not a single-shot composer is shown by the success, following *Faust,* of his *Mireille* (created by Marie Miolan-Carvalho at the Théâtre Lyrique in 1864 and now a staple of the Paris Opéra-Comique) and *Roméo et Juliette* (1867), currently in the repertoire of many of the world's leading opera houses.

NOTES ON PERFORMANCE

There are, considering the length of *Faust,* remarkably few cuts; and most of them — such as the deletion of certain pages for chorus in the Kermesse scene — have tended to be restored in modern performance. One passage so seldom heard as to have remained practically unknown returned in the Metropolitan Opera revival of 1965-'66, when Marguerite's aria at the spinning wheel — after she has been deserted by Faust — aroused a cordial interest. Only the answering cavatina sung by Siébel in this same tableau (which precedes the Church Scene) is still omitted.

As for the ballet, it provides the one note of glitter in an opera known otherwise for its scenic sobriety. More often than not, since this chapter has little relation dramatically to the rest of the work, it is omitted . . . but *Faust* loses thereby in visual contrast. It has been darkly alleged, wihout any documentation to prove the rumor, that not Gounod but Delibes provided the additional ballet music of 1869. Whatever the truth — apparently weighted in favor of Gounod — the sequence is academic in sound, frankly in the mood of a *divertissement*. When, as sometimes happens in modern production, expressionistic dance is grafted onto this slight and stylized musical base, an imbalance can result. *Faust* may best be served by presenting the work for what it is: a winsome period piece, conventional in design, touching in sentiment. For the deeper aspects of Goethe's play, one must turn to other adaptations.

ROBERT LAWRENCE

CAST OF CHARACTERS

FAUST . . . . Tenor

MÉPHISTOPHÉLÈS . . . . Bass

VALENTIN, Marguerite's brother . . . . Baritone

WAGNER, a student . . . . Baritone

MARGUERITE . . . . Soprano

SIEBEL, a youth . . . . Soprano

MARTHE SCHWERLEIN . . . . Contralto or Mezzo-Soprano

Soldiers, Students, Villagers, Dancers, Demons

PLACE: A village in Germany

TIME: Sixteenth century

Index

Faust.

CH. GOUNOD.

Introduction.

Printed in U.S.A.

Act I.
SCENE 1
Nº 1. Scene and Chorus.

It is night. Faust, alone, is seated at a table covered with books and parchments; an open book lies before him. His lamp is nearly extinguished.

Faust. Recit. **Andante**

Rien!!..
En vain j'inter-roge, en mon ar-den-te veil-le,   La na-
In vain!
In vain I have stud-ied the myst'ry of cre-a-tion,   In my

6

46104

luit!.. Ô mort! quand vien-dras-tu m'a-bri-ter sous ton
day! — O Death! When will you come And re-lease me from my

Allegro. *(picking up a flask from the table)*

ai - le?
bond- -age?

Eh bien! puis-que la mort me
Well then!— If you a-void my

fuit,
path,

Pour-quoi n'i-rais-je pas vers el-le?..
Why should I not go forth to meet you?

Wind

(He pours the content of the flask into a goblet.)

Andante maestoso.

Ob., Cl., etc.

Sa- lut!— ô mon der-nier ma-
To you,— last of my days on

8

tin! _____ Sa - lut! ô mon der-nier ma - tin! _____ J'ar -
earth, _____ To you I bid my last fare - well! _____ I

ri - - ve sans ter - reur _____ Au ter - - me du vo -
face _____ with-out a fear _____ The end- - ing of my

ya - - ge; Et je suis, a - vec ce breu - va - ge, Le seul
jour - - ney, For this draft will make me the mas - ter Of my

maî - tre de mon des - tin! Je suis, je suis, a - vec ce breu -
des - ti - ny here on earth. This draft, this draft will make me the

(As he raises the goblet to his lips, the voices of
women singing are heard outside.)

va - ge, ___ Le seul maî - tre de mon des - tin! _____
mas - ter Of my des - ti - ny here on earth. _____

Brass

ff

46104

san - te Sou - rit___ aux mois-sons; Le ruisseau mur-mu - re,
joic - ing In dawn's___ gold - en smile. Near the brook and bow - er

La fleur s'ouvre au jour,___ Tou-te la _ na - tu - re S'é-veille à _ l'a -
Coos the tur - tle dove,___ Ev -'ry bud - ding flow - er A - wak - en -

mour! Tou-te la _ na - tu - re S'é - veille à l'a - mour!___
love,___ Ev -'ry bud - ding flow - er A - wak - ens to love.___

Faust.

Vains é - chos de la joie___ hu - mai - ne, Pas - sez,___ pas -
Emp -ty ech - oes of world - ly pleas - ure, A - way.___

sez vo - tre che - min!.. ___ Pas - sez, ___ pas -
way! Go far a - way!___ A - way,___ a -

№ 2. Duet.

Allegro agitato. (♩ = 130)   Faust.   Recit.

F.

Mais ce Dieu,— que peut-il pour
But this God,— what can he do for

Piano.   *ff*   *ff*

moi?..   Me ren-dra-t-il l'a - mour,— la jeu-
me?   Can he re - store my youth— and its

ff   *ff*

Andante maestoso.

nes-se   et la foi?—   Mau-di -tes soyez-vous, ô vo-luptés humai - nes!
pas-sion And my faith?—   A curse on all the joys, The lust for hu man pleas-ure,

ff   *fp*

Mau - di -tes soient les chaînes Qui me font ramper i - ci - bas!— Mau - dit
Ac-curs-ed be the fet -ters Chain-ing me so firm - ly to life!— Be ac-

fp   *fp*

soit   tout ce qui nous leur - re, Vain es - poir qui passe a - vec
cursed what man finds al - lur - ing, Emp-ty hopes, so brief - ly en-

fp

gui-se? L'é-pée au cô-té, la plume au chapeau, L'escar-cel - le
please you? A sword at my side, A purse full of gold, On my cap— a

un poco animato

plei-ne, un ri-che manteau sur l'é-pau-le; en som-me, Un vrai gentil-
feath-er, The el - e -gant cloak I am wear-ing, I fan-cy, it's ver-y be-

Poco Meno mosso

hom- — -me! Eh
com - -ing! I

colla voce

bien! doc-teur, que me veux-tu? Vo-yons; par - le!.. Te fais-je
ask you, Sir, what do you want? Speak up, Doc - tor! Are you a-

Poco più mosso Faust. Mephistopheles. Faust.

peur?_ Non._ Dou-tes-tu de ma puis-san-ce? Peut-
fraid?_ No. _ Are you doubt-ful of my pow-er? I

46104

Faust.

suite __ à __ la por - te!
miss __ him __ so light - ly!

Et que peux
Are you all

colla voce

Vlns.

Allegro.

f

tu pour moi?
pow-er-ful?

Mephistopheles.

Tout,.. tout... __ mais
Yes, __ yes . . . . __ But

Moderato.

dis-moi d'abord Ce que tu
first I must know What you de-

Que fe-rai - je de la ri -
What on earth would I do with

Poco animato.

veux; est - ce de l'or? _____
sire. Could it be gold? _____

ches - se?
rich - es?

Bon, je vois où le bât te bles -
Ah, I think that I know __ what ails

20

sirs! ___ À moi ___ l'é - ner - gi - e Des ins - tincts puis-
vine! ___ Oh give ___ me the glow - ing flame of youth - ful

cresc.

sants, ___ Et la folle or - gi - e Du cœur ___ et des
fire, ___ That pas - sion - ate yearn - ing For love ___ and de -

sens! ___ Ar - den - te jeu - nes - se, À moi ___ tes dé -
sire! ___ The youth ___ and the ar - dor, The pain ___ and the

p   *cresc.*

sirs, ___ A moi ___ ton i - vres - se, À moi ___ tes plai -
bliss, ___ The joy ___ of the lov - er, The thrill ___ of a

f

rit.

sirs, ___ À moi ton i - vres - se, À moi ___ tes_ plai -
kiss, ___ The joy of the lov - er, The pain ___ and_ the

colla voce

46104

24

26

28

à moi___ tes plai - sirs!
The joy___ and the bliss!

à toi___ ses plai - sirs!
The joy___ and the bliss!

sempre f

(They rush off. The curtain falls.)

Nº 3. Grand Chorus.

The Fair. (Kermesse.)

At one of the city gates, at the left an inn with a sign showing the wine god Bacchus.

SCENE 2

Vin ou biè - re, Bière ou vin, Que mon
Fill your glass - es, fill your Stein, Be it

32

ver - re   Soit   plein!   Sans   ver - go - gne,   Coup   sur
beer _ or   be it   wine,   Strong   or _   mel - low,   we   don't _

Wagner.

Jeune a - dep - te   Du ton -
When _ the _ wine - jug goes a -

coup,   Un _ i   vro - gne _   Boit   tout!
mind,   For _ we   drink   an - y _   kind.

p

stacc.

Fl., etc

Bn.

neau, N'en   ex - cep - te   Que   l'eau!   Que   ta   gloi - re,   Tes a -
round, We   can _ al - ways   be _   found!   On - ly _   wa - ter   we _ dis -

mours, Soient   de   boi - re   Tou - jours!
dain, Drink - ing   keeps _ us _ sound and   sane!

BASSES I (Students).

Jeune a - dep - te   Du ton -
When _ the _ wine - jug goes a -

46104

neau, N'en ex - cep - te Que l'eau! Que ta gloi - re, Tes a -
round, We can al - ways be found! On - ly wa - ter we dis -

mours, Soient de boi - re Tou - jours!
dain, Drink - ing keeps us sound and sane!

BASSES II (Soldiers).

Fil - les ou for - te - res - ses, C'est tout
Wom - en, for - ti - fi - ca - tions, We at -

un, mor - bleu! Vieux burgs, jeu - nes maî - tres - ses, Sont pour
tack them all! Cas - tles or young maid - ens, Both are

nous un jeu! Ce - lui qui sait _____ s'y _ pren - dre, Sans trop _
bound to fall. And as for the fe - male gen - der, They are _

de _ fa - çon, Les o - blige à _____ se ren - dre En pa _ yant ran -
eas - y _ prey, We in - duce them to _ sur - ren - der For _ a - ran - som

çon! En pa - yant ran - çon! _____
pay, For _ a - ran - som pay! _____

Valve horn

Horn

TENORS I. (Burghers).

Aux jours de di - manche et de fê - te, J'aime à par - ler guerre et combats;
Sun - day is my one day of lei - sure, When I en - joy gos - sip of war.

Vlns.

Tan - dis que les peu - ples là - bas Se cas - sent la
I'm too old to fight an - y more, I want quiet

tê - te. Je vais m'asseoir sur les cô-teaux Qui sont voi-sins de la ri -
pleas - ure. I love to sit un - der the sky, Watch-ing the shin-ing riv - er

vie - re, Et je vois pas - ser les ba-teaux En vi - dant mon
flow - ing And the pret - ty boats pass-ing by, See them com - ing and

ver - re! Je vais mas-seoir sur les cô-teaux
go - ing! I love to sit un - der the sky,

Qui sont voi - sins de la ri - viè - re, Et je vois pas -
Watch-ing the shin-ing riv - er flow - ing And the pret - ty

36

46104

46104

(to the older women)

De vo - tre co - lè - re, Nous ne crai - gnons
You are on - ly jeal - ous, But we do not

bien!
mind,

Vi - dons, vi - dons un ver - re de
Let's leave our cares and trou - bles be -

Vo - yez leur co - lè - re, Vo - yez leur main -
Oth - ers will be jeal - ous But we do not

vin, Que mon ver - re Soit
stein, Be it beer or be it

plai - re, Nous sa - vons leur plaire En un tour de
sol - dier, Oth - ers will be jeal - ous, We do not

rien!
mind!

So - yez sans ver - go - gne, Comme ils sont sans
Flirt - ing with those fel - lows, We are not so

vin!
hind.

tien!
mind,

plein! Sans ver - go - gne, Coup sur
wine. Strong or mel - low, we don't

main! Al - lons en be - so - gne, Sans peur ni ver -
mind. We know how to woo them, Gal - lant - ly pur -

44

46104

49

46104

Nº 4. Scene, Recitative, and Cavatina

56

Siebel

Sur moi tu peux comp-ter!
On me you may de-pend.

TENORS.

Comp-te sur nous aus-si!
You are a faith-ful friend.

BASSES.

Moderato.

Cavatina.*   Valentine.

Poco Andante. ♩ = 76

A-vant de quit-ter ces lieux,
Now that I must say good-by

Sol na-tal de mes a-ïeux,
To my home and na-tive sky,

À toi, Seigneur et
Lord, may I en-

Roi des cieux,
trust to Thee

Ma sœur je con-
My sis-ter so

46104   * The French words of this Cavatina are by O. Pradere.

58

46104

62

Nº 4a. Song of the Golden Calf

66

Nº 5. Scene and Chorus.

70

(He tastes the wine and throws it from the cup.)

Peuh! que ton vin est mau-
Phew! What a fla-vor-less

cresc.
ff

Andante.

vais! Per-met-tez - moi de vous en of-frir de ma
wine! If you al - low, I will or - der some from my

dim. Cornets
p

Allegretto.

ca - ve. (striking on a barrel, surmounted by a
cel - lar. figure of Bacchus, which serves as a
sign for the inn)
Wind

Ho - là! sei - gneur Bac-chus,
Ho there! Bac-chus, my friend!

pp
Tromb.

(Wine flows from the barrel.)

à boi - re!
The fin - est!
Vlns.

pp

74

76

46104

S. de, C'est u - ne croix qui de l'en - fer nous___
vil! Be - hold this cross which guards us all from—

V. de, C'est u - ne croix qui de l'en - fer nous
vil! Be - hold this cross which guards us all from

W. de, C'est u - ne croix qui de l'en - fer nous
vil! Be - hold this cross which guards us all from

de, C'est u - ne croix qui de l'en - fer nous___
vil! Be - hold this cross which guards us all from___

S. gar - -de!
e - - -vil!

(Everybody leaves. Mephistopheles remains, subdued.)

V. gar - -de!
e - - -vil!

W. gar - -de!
e - - -vil!

gar - -de!
e - - -vil!

Tutti

ff

Nº 6. Waltz and Chorus.

Tempo di Valzer. (♩.=72)

yeux!
pear.

(Students and girls enter arm in arm, followed by musicians.
The burghers and towns-people are behind them. The musi-
cians begin to play.)

Piano.

Tutti

coll'8va ad lib.

Chorus.

SOPRANOS.

Ain - si que la bri - se lé - gè - re Sou - lève en é - pais tour-bil-
Light and swift as sum-mer-y breez-es, Our feet bare-ly touch on the

TENORS.

Ain - si que la bri - se lé - gè - re Sou - lève en é - pais tour-bil-
Light and swift as sum-mer-y breez-es, Our feet bare-ly touch on the

BASSES.

Ain - si que la bri - se lé - gè - re Sou - lève en é - pais tour-bil-
Light and swift as sum-mer-y breez-es, Our feet bare-ly touch on the

Vlns.

84

46104

(Siebel recoils from Mephistopheles who chases him around the scene behind the dancers.)

Me: vous voi - là!
On your way!

(Margarita crosses the stage.)

Andantino (♩=69)

(One beat equals a measure preceding.)

Faust *(accosting Margarita)*

F: Ne permettrez-vous pas, ma bel - le demoi-sel-le,
Will you per-mit me pray, My fair and gra-cious la - dy?

F: Qu'on vous of-fre le bras pour fai - re le che - min?..
May I give you my arm And es - cort on your way?

Margarita.

Ms: Non, mon-sieur! je ne suis demoi - sel - le, ni bel - le, demoi -
No, my lord, I am nei - ther a la - dy Nor gra - cious, nei - ther

92

46104

SOPRANOS. (1st Group of young girls) (2d Group.)

Qu'est-ce donc? Margue - ri - te, Qui de ce beau sei -
What was that? Mar-ga - ri-ta re - fused to be es -

gneur re - fu - se la con-dui-te.
cort - -ed By that no-ble strang-er.

TENORS.

Val -sons!. val - sons!. Val - sons!.
Danc-ing! Danc-ing! Waltz-ing!

BASSES.

Val - sons!. val _ sons!. Val - sons!.
Danc-ing! Danc-ing! Waltz-ing!

Chorus.

cresc.

96

46104

98

46104

100

46104

swing, / rir, — Un Dieu les en trai — — ne: / The danc — — ers are whirl — — ing,

C'est — le plai — sir! Jus — qu'à perdre ha — / Plea — — — sure is king! See how they are

lei — ne, Jus — qu'à mou — rir, Un / swirl — ing, Wild — ly they swing, The

Dieu les en - traî - - - ne:
danc - - ers are whirl - - - ing,

Dieu les en - traî - - - ne:
danc - - ers are whirl - - - ing,

Dieu les en - traî - - ne:
danc - - ers are whirl - - - ing,

C'est le plai - sir!
Plea - - - - sure is king!

C'est le plai - sir!
Plea - - - sure is king!

C'est le plai - sir!
Plea - - - - sure is king!

coll'8va ad lib.

End of Act I.

Act II.

Nº 7. Intermezzo and Song.

Margarita's Garden

A wall at back, with a little door. A bower at left, a house at right, with a window toward the audience. Trees, shrubs, etc.

Moderato quasi andante.(♩ = 60 to 66)

104

46104

107

46104

Scene and Recitative.

110

vais vous chercher un tré - sor Plus merveil - leux, plus riche en -
vie with the flow-ers of Sie - bel, Some-thing so rare no words can

Me.
F.

cor___ Que tous ceux qu'el - le voit en rê - ve! Lais-se-moi!
tell,___ Far be-yond all im-ag-in-a - tion. Go a - way!

Faust.

Mephistopheles.

J'o - bé - is! Daignez m'attendre i -
As you say. But you wait here for

(He leaves.)

ci. aux fleurs de votre é - lè - ve, Pour te - nir compa - gnie Je
me. And find a lit - ting pres-ent To in the mean-time I'll go

Nº 8. Cavatina.

114

Larghetto.

46104

118

Scene.

46104

Nº 9. Scene and Aria.

(*Margarita* enters through the little door
and comes silently to the front.)

Margarita.

Je voudrais bien sa-voir quel é-tait ce jeune homme;
Who was the hand-some man Who so bold-ly ad-dressed me?

Si c'est un grand sei-
Was he ___ a no-ble

gneur, et comment il se nom — me?
lord? ___ And why has he so im-pressed me?

Song.
The King of Thule.

Moderato maestoso. (♩ = 72) (*She sits down at her spinning wheel and as she spins she sings an old ballad.*)

Margarita.

poco ritenuto

Il é - tait un
Once a king in

Roi de Thulé,___ Qui, jus-qu'à la tom - be fi - dè - le,
Thu - le of old,___ Faith-ful un - to death to his la - dy,

Eut, en sou-ve-nir de sa bel - le, U - ne coupe en or ci - se -
Kept, to hon-or her cher - ished mem-'ry, By his side a chal - ice of

rit.

Andante.   (*breaking off*)

lé.___ Il a - vait bon - ne
gold.___ He was kind - ly and

122

46104

123

46104

124

46104

vrais!.. ma main tremble!.. Pour-quoi? Je ne fais, en l'ouvrant, rien de mal, je sup-
in it? I am fright-ened. But why? I won't do an-y harm if I o-pen the

(opens the cover)

po - se! O Dieu! que de bi-joux! est-ce un rê - ve char-
cov-er. Ah no!— It can't be true! Is it real or a

mant Qui m'é - blou - it,— ou si je veil - le? Mes yeux n'ont ja - mais
vi - sion that I see,— Or am I dream-ing? I've nev-er seen such

Allegro non troppo.

vu de ri - ches - se pa - reil - le!
jew - els So pre - cious and gleam - ing!

(Puts down the casket and kneels to look at the jewels.)

126

46104

The Jewel Song.

128

46104

toi,   Ce n'est plus toi,_____ C'est la fil - le d'un roi, Qu'on sa -
you,   This is not you!_____ It's a prin - cess or queen Pass-ing

lue au pas - sa - ge!   Ah s'il é - tait i - ci!
by in her glo - ry!   How hap - py I would be

S'il me vo - yait ainsi!   Comme u - ne de-moi-sel - le
If he could look at me!   Now if I were to meet him,

Il me trouve - rait bel - le,   Ah!_____
Smil - ing - ly I would greet him,   Ah!_____

_____ Comme u - ne de - moi - selle Il me trou - ve - rait bel - le,
_____ Then he would bow to me In all my roy - al splen - dor,

130

Comme u – ne de – moi – selle Il me trou – ve – rait bel – le!
Then he would bow to me In all my roy – al splen – dor!

colla voce

Margarita. *(She goes back to the jewel case)*

A – che – vons la mé – ta – mor – pho – se.
Now I'll try all the oth – er jew – els!

Il me tarde en – cor d'essay – er Le bra – ce –
All I have to do is put on The pret – ty

Poco più lento.

let et le col – lier!
brace – let and the pearls.

trem.

46104

131

46104

belle en ce mi-roir! Est-ce toi,— Mar-gue-
beau-ti-ful to see! Is it you,— Mar-ga-

ri-te, Est-ce toi? Réponds-moi, réponds-moi,
ri-ta? Is it true? Is it true? Is it true?

réponds, réponds, réponds vi-te! Ah! s'il é-tait i-ci!
Is it real-ly Mar-ga-ri-ta? How hap-py I would be

S'il me vo-yait ainsi, Comme u-ne de-moi-sel-le
If he could look at me! Now if I were to meet him

Il me trouve - rait bel - le,   Ah!
Smil - ing - ly I would greet him,   Ah!

cresc.

_Comme u - ne de - moi - selle Il me trou - ve - rait bel - le! Comme u - ne de - moi-
_Then he would bow to me In all my roy - al splen - dor, Then he would bow to

f   dim.   p

rit.   a tempo

selle, Il me trou - ve - rait bel - le!   Mar - gue - ri - te,
me In all my roy - al splen - dor!   Mar - ga - ri - ta,

a tempo

pp   colla voce   p   cresc. -

Ce n'est plus toi,   Ce n'est plus ton vi - sa - ge!
This is not you!   That's a prin - cess of sto - ry!

134

46104

Nº 10. Scene and Quartet.

136

là _____ le ca-deau d'un Sei-gneur a-mou-reux! ___ Mon cher é-
deed, _____ some ad-mir-er must have put them there. ___ My hus-band

poux ja-dis ___ é - tait moins gé-né - reux!
nev - er gave ___ me a pres-ent so rare! *(Mephistopheles and Faust enter.)*

Mephistopheles (*saluting*)   Martha.

Da-me Mar-the Schwerlein, s'il vous plaît?   Qui m'ap-
Mad-am Mar-tha Schwert-lein, I be - lieve?   Who are

Mephistopheles.

pel - le?   Par-don d'o-ser ain - si nous pré - sen - ter   chez
you, sir?   For-give us for in - trud-ing in this way   on

(aside to Faust)

vous!   (Vous vo - yez qu'elle a fait bon accueil aux bi -
you!   Now you see what a box full of jew-els can

46104

137

46104

142

té!   Sans a - mis,   sans pa - rents,   sans
do.   With-out friends,   all a - lone,   Un -

Martha.

fem - me!   Ah!   Ce - la sied en -
mar - ried,   ah!   When you're young that's

Fl. & Vlns.

pp

core aux beaux jours,   Ce - la sied en - core aux beaux jours!
all ver - y fine,   When you're young that's all ver - y fine,

Mais plus tard,   plus tard!   com-bien il est tris - te
But you'll see,   you'll see   how sad it is lat - er

De vieillir seul,   en é - go - ïs - te,
When you are old,   a lone-ly bach - 'lor,

150

cet - te vieille im - pi - to - ya - ble, De force ou de
That old shrew won't be con - tent - ed Un - til some-one

gré, je crois, Al - lait é - pou-ser le dia - -
mar - ries her, E - ven if it were the dev - -

Martha. (*off-stage*)
Cher sei - gneur!__
Dear-est sir!__

Faust. (*off-stage*)
Mar-gue - ri - te!
Mar-ga - ri - ta!

ble! Ser - - vi -
il. Go your

Cher sei - gneur!
Dear-est sir!__

Mar-gue-ri - te!..
Mar-ga - ri - ta!

teur! Ser - vi - teur!__
way! Go your way!__

pp

Scene.

Il é-tait temps! Sous le feuil-la - ge
And none too soon! Un - der the fall - ing

som - bre Voi - ci nos a-mou-reux qui re - vien-nent!.. C'est
shad - ows The lov - ers are re - turn - ing to - geth - er. All's

bien! Gar-dons nous de trou - bler
well. Let us not in - ter - fere

un si doux en - tre - tien! With
With a love so sin - cere!

157

158

46104

№ 11. Duet.

Andante. (♩ = 50) **Margarita.** (*returning with Faust*)

Il se fait tard, a-dieu!
It's ver-y late! Good night.

Faust.

Quoi! je t'implore en vain! At - tends!
Must I im-plore in vain? O stay!

Lais - se ta main s'ou-bli'- er dans la mien - ne.
Let me but hold your dear hand in my own.

Lais - se-moi, lais - se-moi
Bless - ed love, bless - ed love,

162

46104

Par - le... parle en - co-re!.. Ah! je t'a -
Dear - est, say you love me! Ah, I a -

rit.

do-re! Pour toi je veux mou-rir, pour toi je veux mou-rir!_
dore you, I live for you a-lone, I live for you a - lone.

rit.

Allegro agitato. (*She tears herself away from his embrace.*)

Ah! par - tez!_
Ah, no more!_

Faust.

Mar - gue - ri - te!
Mar - ga - ri - ta!

Mar - gue -
Mar - ga -

Allegro agitato. ($\quad$ = 76)

Ah! par - tez!_
Ah, no more!_

Je chan-cel - le!
I am fright ened!

ri - te!
ri - ta!

cru-el - le...
I beg you!

Me sé - pa -
Don't make me

cresc.

168

46104

(Margarita, hastening toward the house, stops for an instant on the threshold and throws a kiss to Faust.)

Margarita.
A - dieu!__ A - dieu!__ Ah!__ fu - yons!__ Ah!__ A - way!__

Faust.
Fé - li - ci - té du ciel!____ Oh ec - sta - sy di - vine!____

Allegro.

(He starts for the garden door. Mephistopheles bars his way.)

Mephistopheles.
Tê - te fol - le! Par bonheur! You're a mad - man! To be sure!

Tu nous é - cou - tais? So you play the spy?

Moderato.
Vous au - riez grand be - It real - ly seems to

Me. soin, doc - teur, Qu'on vous ren - vo - yât à l'é -
me, my friend, That some - one should send you to

Faust. Mephistopheles.
Me. co - le!.. Laisse-moi! Daignez seu-lement é - cou-ter un mo -
F. school a - gain. Go a - way! At least wait a mo-ment Un-til you have

ff pp

Me. ment, Ce qu'el-le va con-ter aux é - toi-les, Cher maî - tre!..
heard What your new love has to say to the stars, Dear mas-ter!

Larghetto. (Più lento di ♩.= 50)
(Margarita opens her window.)

Me. Te - nez! ___
See there! ___

Clar.
Ob.
pp
Horns

tu – re Me re – di-sent en chœur_ «Il t'ai – me!
a – tion Are re – peat-ing the words:_ "He loves _ you!_

Il _ t'ai – me!» Ah! _ qu'il est doux de
He _ loves _ you!" Ah, _ what a joy _ in

vi – vre! _ Le ciel me sou – rit;_ L'air m'en
liv – ing! _ The night fills my heart _ with its

i – vre, _ l'air m'en – i – vre!
glo – ry _ and _ en – chant – ment!

Est – ce de plai-sir et d'a – mour Que la feuil-le tremble et _ pal
Ev –'ry-where with plea-sure and love _ All the leaves are trem – bling and

End of Act II.

Act III.
Entr'acte and Recitative.
SCENE 1
Margarita's Room

180

Adagio. Margarita.

El-les ne sont plus
They all have gone a-

là... je ri-ais a-vec el-les Au-tre-fois... maintenant...
way... Once I shared in their laugh-ter, Long a-go... but no more...

Allegretto vivo.
SOPRANOS (off-stage)

Le ga-lant é-tran-ger s'en-fuit et court en-
The gal-lant strang-er ran a-way! Where did he

cor! Ah! ah! ah! ah! ah! ah! ah! ah! ah! ah! ah! ah!
go? Ha ha! ha ha! ha ha ha ha ha ha ha ha!

46104

№ 12. The Spinning-wheel Song.
Scene.

Moderato. Recit.

Marg. El - les se ca - chaient! ah! cru - el - les!
They have gone a - way!_ Ah, they scorn me!

Je ne trouvais pas d'outrage assez fort, Ja-dis, pour les péchés des
Not so long a - go I could not find words too strong for oth-er peo-ple's

autres! Un jour vient_ où l'on est sans pi-tié pour les nôtres! Je ne
vic - es, and to - day_ it is they who will show me no pit-y. In my

suis que hon - te à mon tour!_ Et pour - tant_
turn I must suf - fer too!_ But it's true,_

Dieu le sait,_ je n'é - tais pas in - fâ - me; Tout
heav-en knows,_ I had no thought of e - - vil; My

ce qui t'entraî - na, mon â - - me, N'é - tait que ten - dresse _ et qu'a -
on - ly wish, my on - ly long - - ing Was love, ten - der love, _ Good and

cresc.

pp

Bn.

(1) ⊕ Andante. (♩ = 72.)

mour! _
true. _

Horns

m.d.

Vln. I.   *Vln. II.*   *Vln. I.*   *Vln. II.*

Margarita.

Il   ne re - vient pas, _   Il   ne re - vient
He   does not re - turn, _   he   does not re -

(1) In the theatre a cut is made between ⊕ and ⊕ on p. 188.

184

46104

raî - tre,   quel - le joi - - e!
fore me,   I would be so hap - - py!

ff

Tempo I.

Hé - las!_____ hé - las!_____ Où donc peut-il ê - tre?
A - las,_____ a - las!_____ o where does he wan-der?

pp

Il ne re - vient pas!_____
He does not_ re - turn!_____

pp

Allegro agitato.

(Siebel enters hurriedly.) (1)

p   *cresc.* - - - - *f*

(1) Dal 𝄋 page 188.

188

(Siebel enters hurriedly.)

Allegro agitato.

mour!
true._

Margarita.

Sie-bel!   Hé-las! vous seul ne me maudissez
Sie-bel!   A - las,   the on - ly faith-ful friend I

Siebel.

Mar-gue-ri-te!   En-cor des pleurs!
Mar-ga - ri - ta!   In tears a - gain!

Moderato.

Siebel.

pas... Je ne suis qu'un enfant;   mais j'ai le cœur d'un homme,   Et je vous ven-ge-
have. I am still ver-y young   But a man in spir-it,   And I swear I'll a-

Margarita.

Qui donc?..
Whom?

rai de son lâche a-ban - don,   Je le tue - rai!   Faut-
venge All the wrong he has   done.   I'll strike him   dead!   You

Cl. & Bn.

46104

190

46104

Margarita

So-yez bé - ni, Sie-bel; votre a-mi-tié m'est douce!
May heav-en smile on you, For you are good to me.

Ceux dont la main cru-el - le me re - pousse N'ont pas fer-mé pour
All those who now dis - dain me as a sin-ner Can still not bar the

moi les por - tes du Saint-lieu!.. J'y vais, pour mon en-fant et pour
way To God who will for - give. I'll go, for my child and for

lui pri - er Dieu!..
him I shall pray!

№ 13. Scene in the Church.

SCENE 2

(*Some women enter the church. Margarita enters after them and kneels.*)

194

Margarita

Ma.

Seig- neur, daignez per - mettre à votre humble ser - van - te   De __
O   Lord,   Thy hum-ble   serv-ant is   ask -ing Thy   mer - cy,   See __

Ma.

__ s'a - genouil - ler de - vant   vous. __
__ me kneel be - fore Thee and   pray. __

(Organ)

46104

196

46104

197

198

46104

Margarita.

Dieu!__ quelle est cet-te voix qui me par-le dans
God,__ what voice comes to me From the shad-ows as-

(Orch.)

pp

Più mosso.

l'ombre? Dieu tout puissant! Quel voi-le sombre Sur moi des-cend?__
cend-ing? Al-might-y God, dark-ness is fall-ing up-on my eyes!__

Chorus of Priests and Boys (*invisible*)
SOPRANOS, TENORS, BASSES.

Quand du Seigneur le jour lui-ra__
When the Judg-ment trum-pets thun-der,__

f(Organ)

(Orch.)

Brass

Sa croix au ciel res-plen-di-ra__
Then the cross shall shine in splen-dor,__

(Organ)

(Orch.)

Et l'u-ni-vers s'é-crou-le-ra!__
And the U-ni-verse pass__ a-way.__

(Organ)

(Orch.)

46104

200

Margarita.

Ma. Hé-las! hé-las!___ ce chant pi - eux est plus ter-rible en-
A-las! A-las!___ Is there no mer-cy in this fear-some

Vlns.

pp

Ma.
Me.

Mephis.

co- -re! Non!___ pour toi Dieu n'a plus de par-
warn- -ing? No!___ For you, no for-give - ness from

Me.

don!___ Pour toi le ciel n'a plus d'au-
God!___ For you, no day will have a

Me.

ro- -re! non!___ non!___
dawn- -ing! No!___ No!___

Chorus of Priests, etc. *(invisible)*

ff

Que di - rai - je a - lors au Sei - gneur,___
Who will help me, Who will guide me?___

Più mosso.

f *(Organ)*

(Orch.)

et les jours pleins d'i - vres - - se!
to the days of en - chant - - ment!

à toi mal - heur!____ à toi l'en -
Your soul is damned! ____ Your soul is

Margarita. *rit.* **Più lento.**

Sei - gneur,____ Sei - gneur! accueil-lez la pri -
O Lord,____ O Lord, I im-plore Thee to

fer!_____
damned!_____
SOPRANOS.

Chorus of Priests, etc. Sei - - gneur, Sei -
TENORS. O Lord, O

(Organ) **Più lento.**

p rit. *(Orch.)*

Nº 14. The Soldiers' Chorus.
SCENE 3

Tempo di marcia.

Piano.

Chorus of Soldiers.

TENORS I.

Dé - po - sons les ar - mes, Dé - po - sons les ar - mes, Dans nos fo -
Now the war is o - ver, Now the war is o - ver; Friends, put your

TENORS II.

Dé - po - sons les ar - mes, Dé - po - sons les ar - mes, Dans nos fo -
Now the war is o - ver, Now the war is o - ver; Friends, put your

BASSES I & II (**Valentine** v.B.I).

Dé - po - sons les ar - mes, Dé - po - sons les ar - mes, Dans nos fo -
Now the war is o - ver, Now the war is o - ver; Friends, put your

p espress.

yers en - fin nous voi - ci re - ve - nus, Nos mè - res en
swords to rest, We are home once a - gain. You moth - ers, be

yers en - fin nous voi - ci re - ve - nus, Nos mè - res en
swords to rest, We are home once a - gain. You moth - ers, be

yers en - fin nous voi - ci re - ve - nus, Nos mè - res en
swords to rest, We are home once a - gain. You moth - ers, be

p

lar - mes, Nos mè - res et nos sœurs ne nous at - ten - dront
hap - py, You sweet-hearts, dry your tears, Have done with grief and

lar - mes, Nos mè - res et nos sœurs ne nous at - ten - dront
hap - py, You sweet-hearts, dry your tears, Have done with grief and

lar - mes, Nos mè - res et nos sœurs ne nous at - ten - dront
hap - py, You sweet-hearts, dry your tears, Have done with grief and

plus Dé-po-sons les ar-mes, Nos mè-res-en lar-mes, Nos
pain. No weep-ing and cry-ing, No mourn-ing-and sigh-ing. You
plus. Dé-po-sons les ar-mes, Nos mè-res en lar-mes, Nos
pain. No weep-ing and cry-ing, No mourn-ing and sigh-ing. You
plus. Dé-po-sons les ar-mes, Nos mè-res en lar-mes, Nos
pain. No weep-ing and cry-ing, No mourn-ing and sigh-ing. You
mè-res et nos sœurs ne nous at-ten-dront plus, Nos mè-res et nos
sweet-hearts, have no fears, We men are home at last; You moth-ers, dry your
mè-res et nos sœurs ne nous at-ten-dront plus, Nos mè-res et nos
sweet-hearts, have no fears, We men are home at last; You moth-ers, dry your
mè-res et nos sœurs ne nous at-ten-dront plus, Nos mè-res et nos
sweet-hearts, have no fears, We men are home at last; You moth-ers, dry your
sœurs ne nous at-ten-dront plus.
tears, The time for grief is past.
sœurs ne nous at-ten-dront plus.
tears, The time for grief is past.
sœurs ne nous at-ten-dront plus.
tears, The time for grief is past.
Fl., Cl., Cornet, etc.

212

46104

Et sous ton ai - le, Sol - dats vain - queurs,___ Di -
We fought like you for the cause of right,___ Our

ri - ge nos pas, en - flam - me nos cœurs!___
spir-its are high, our hon - or is bright.___

Vers___ nos fo - yers___ Hâ - tons le
Now___ we are home,___ our du - ty

Cl. Horns etc.

p Saxhorns, Bn., etc.

pas, On nous attend, la paix est fai - te,___ Plus___ de sou -
done, The time has come for cel-e -bra - tion.___ Let___ us re -

46104

coeurs! Di - ri - ge nos pas, di - ri - ge nos pas,_____ di - ri - ge nos
bright. Our spir-it is high, our spir-it is high,_____ our spir-it is

pas,_____ en - flam - me nos coeurs!_____
high, _____ our hon - or is bright._____

(The soldiers march off. Valentine and Siebel remain.)

Recit.

№ 15. Scene and Serenade.

226

46104

228

46104

230

Nº 16. Trio. The Duel.

233

46104

234

46104

toi qui pré - ser - vas mes jours, ____ Toi qui me
you, the trea-sured med - al I wore, ____ Once cher-ished

viens de Mar - gue - ri - te, Je ne veux plus de ton se - cours, Je ne veux
gift of Mar - ga - ri - ta, I do not want you an - y - more, __ I do not

plus de ton se - cours, ____ Mé - dail - - le mau -
want you an - y - more! ____ Ac - curs - - ed me -

cresc. - - - -

(He throws the medal away.)

di - te! Je ne veux plus de ton se - cours! __
dal - lion, I spurn your help for - ev - er - more. __

Mephistopheles (*aside*)

Tu t'en re - pen - ti -
There you are ver - y

fp   Ob. & Cl.

238

46104

Nº 17. The Death of Valentine.

M.

dez, _____ le voi - ci!
look, _____ here he is.

dez, _____ le voi - ci!
look, _____ here he is.

SOPRANOS.

Il n'est pas en-cor mort, ___ on di-rait qu'il re-
He is hurt but a - live, ___ I can see he is

TENORS.

Il n'est pas en-cor mort, ___ on di-rait qu'il re-
He is hurt but a - live, ___ I can see he is

BASSES.

mu - e! Vite, ap-pro-chons! Il faut le se-cou-rir! Ap-pro-chons, ap-pro-
breath-ing. Quick, o - ver here, It's cer-tain he needs help, Hur-ry up, hur-ry

mu - e! Vite, ap-pro-chons! Il faut le se-cou-rir! Ap-pro-chons, ap-pro-
breath-ing. Quick, o - ver here, It's cer-tain he needs help, Hur-ry up, hur-ry

247

46104

248

46104

250

46104

(He dies.)

tombe en_____ sol - dat.
sol - dier_____ and brave.

Più lento d'adagio.

SOPRANOS.

Que le Sei - gneur ait son âme et par - donne au pê - cheur._____
May God have mer - cy on him and his soul And for - give._____

TENORS.

Que le Sei - gneur ait son âme et par - donne au pê - cheur._____
May God have mer - cy on him and his soul And for - give._____

BASSES.

Più lento d'adagio.

Tempo I.

Clar.

Fl. & Ob.

Clar.

End of Act III.

Act IV.

№ 18. The Walpurgis Night.

SCENE 1

Allegro.

Andante maestoso.

Piano.

pp

cresc.

f

dim.

p

Mephistopheles.

Me.

Jus-qu'aux premiers feux du ma - tin, ＿＿＿ À l'a - bri des re - gards pro-
Till the morn-ing glows in the sky, ＿＿＿ Hid-den far from pro-fane mor-tal

Me.

fa - nes, Je t'offre u - ne pla - ce au fes-tin Des rei - nes et ＿ des
glanc ＿ es, As my guest of hon - or You shall feast with he - ro - ines ＿ of

cresc.

colla voce

cour - ti - sa - - nes.
great ro - manc - - es. **Maestoso assai.**

ff

Ped. ✻

Chorus. **SOPRANOS.** *f*

Que les cou - pes s'em - plis - sent, Au
As the wine flows a - bound - ing The

nom des an - ciens dieux,____ Que les airs re - ten -
an - cient gods we hail,____ Joy - ous songs are re -

262

46104

cou - pes s'em - plis - sent, Au nom des an - ciens
wine flows a - bound - ing, The an - cient gods we

Dieux, _____ Que les airs re - ten - tis - sent
hail, _____ Joy - ous songs are re - sound - ing

Faust.

Vains re - mords! ri - si - ble fo -
Vain re - morse! I laugh at my

De nos ac - cords jo - yeux! _____
Till _____ the sky grows pale. _____

li - e! Il est temps _____ que _____ mon cœur ou -
fol - ly! Now's the time _____ to _____ for - get your

*) The Ballet added for the Grand Opéra begins with this measure. (See Appendix.)

46104

266

46104

268

46104

*) The Ballet ends on this measure.

46104

(*Faust sees a vision of Margarita.*)

Mephistoph.
Qu'as-tu donc?
Have you gone mad?

Faust.
Ne la vois-tu pas,
Don't you see her there,

là...devant nous,— muette et blê - me?.. Quel étrange or - ne-
there ... Be fore our eyes — so pale and si - lent? What a strange thing she

veux!
mand!

№ 19. Final Trio.

Prison Scene.

SCENE 2

Moderato maestoso. (♩ = 72)

Piano.

Faust (*to Mephistopheles*) **Mephistopheles.**

Va t'en!
A - way!

Le jour va lui - re; on
The day is dawn-ing; The

Moderato.

p Cornets etc.

dresse l'é-cha - faud,_ Dé - ci - de sans re -tard Mar-gue-rite a te
scaf-fold is pre-pared,_ You must at once per-suade Mar-ga- ri - ta to

mf

sui - - vre Le geô - lier dort,_
join you. The guard's a - sleep,_

pp

Faust.

Lais - se -
Leave us a -

voi - ci les clefs, il faut que ta main d'homme la dé - li - vre.
I have his key, Your hu-man hand is need-ed to free her.

278

46104

Ô tor - tu - re! Ô sour - ce de re - grets et d'é - ter - nels re -
what tor - ture! O foun - tain of re - gret and ev - er - last - ing re -

Moderato.

mords! C'est el - le, la voi - ci,
morse! I see her, she is here,

la dou - ce cré - a - tu - re, Je - tée au fond d'u - ne pri -
That sweet and love - ly be - ing, Im - pris - oned in this dun - geon

son comme u - ne vi - le cri - mi - nel - le! Le désespoir
here, Like an - y crim - i - nal of - fend - er! And her despair

é - ga - ra sa rai - son! Son pauvre enfant,
has be - wil - dered her mind! And her poor child,

ô Dieu! son pauvre enfant tu - é,_ tu - é par el - le!
o God. Her wretch-ed child is dead,_ Killed by its moth - er!

Margarita. *(waking)* Recit.

Mar - gue - ri - te! Mar - gue - ri - te! Ah! c'est la voix du bien-ai -
Mar-ga - ri - ta! Mar-ga - ri - ta! Ah! That is my be-lov-ed's

mé!__ À son ap - pel mon cœur c'est ra - ni - mé!
voice!_ Hear-ing him call, my heart wak-ens a - gain!

Faust.

Mar - gue - ri - te!
Mar-ga - ri - ta!

Vlns.

Margarita.

Au mi - lieu de vos é - clats de ri - re, Dé - mons qui m'en-tou -
Sweet and clear, o - ver your bursts of laugh - ter, You de - mons ev - er

t'ai - me, Mal - gré l'ef - fort mê - me Du dé - mon mo -
love you De - spite all en - deav - ors Of the e - vil

queur,___ Je t'ai re - trou - vé - e, je t'ai re - trou -
fiend.___ Once more I have found you, Once more I have

vé - e, Te voi - là sau - vé - e,
found you. I have come to save you,

Te voi - là sau - vé - e, C'est moi, viens, viens___ sur mon
I have come to save you. My love, come, come___ to my

Tempo del Valzer. *(He attempts to take her away; she gently avoids his arms.)* Margarita *(her mind wandering)*

coeur! _____ At - tends! _____
arms. _____ Ah, wait! _____

Voi - ci la ru -
Do you re - mem -

- e Où tu m'as vu - e Pour la pre - miè - re
- - ber There in the street _____ Where you and I first

fois, _____ Où vo - tre
met? _____ Where once your

main _____ o - sa presque ef - fleu - rer _____ mes
hand _____ Pressed my own As you said _____ to

Andantino.

doigts. «Ne permettrez - vous pas, — ma bel - le de-moi -
me: "Will you per-mit me, pray, — My fair and gra-cious

sel - le, Qu'on vous of-fre le bras pour fai - re le che - min?»
la - dy? May I give you my arm And es - cort on your way?"

Vcl.

«Non, mon - sieur, — je ne suis de-moi - sel - le ni bel - le, de - moi -
"No, my lord, — I am nei - ther a la - dy nor gra - cious, nei - ther

pp

poco rit.

sel - le ni bel - le, Et je n'ai pas be - soin qu'on me don - ne la
la - dy nor gra - cious, Nor do I need To be es - cort- ed on my

colla voce

294

46104

№ 19a. Apotheosis

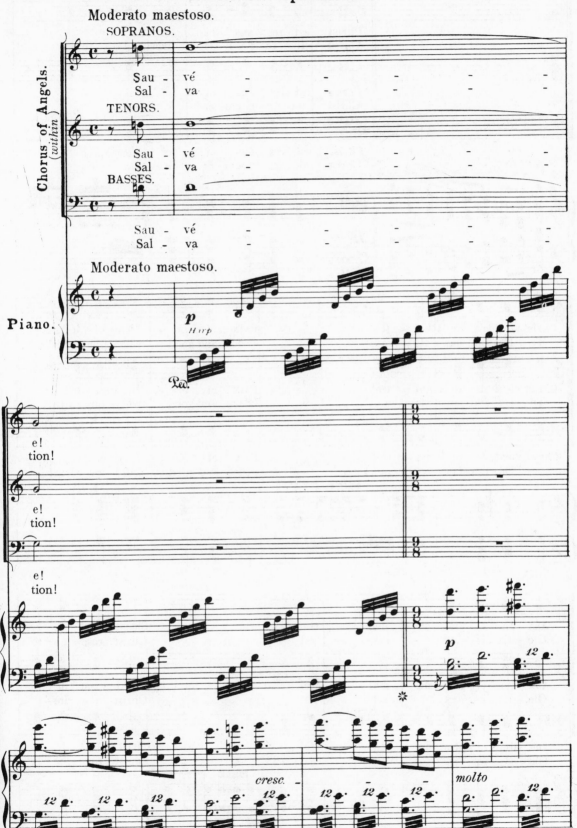

298

46104

End of the Opera.

Faust.
Ballet.

Allegretto, Mouvement de Valse.

1.

313

46104